STEMinists

The Lifework of 12 Women Scientists and Engineers

STEMinists: The Lifework of 12 Women Scientists and Engineers

Xóchitl Justice Press, San Francisco, CA

Library of Congress Control Number: 2018932203

ISBN: 9781942001782

First Edition March 2018

10 9 8 7 6 5 4 3 2 1

STEMinists
The Lifework of 12 Women Scientists and Engineers

Editors: Diana J. Arya & Jasmine K. McBeath
Series Editor: Nicola A. McClung

Written and illustrated by participants in the Curie-osity Project

Deana Aguilera-Arroyo
Aaliyah Anaya
Lily Angeles
Dylan Bouma
Aiyana Brown
Sloane Brown
Sophia Copeland
Kiare Edwards
Anabel Gonzales
Lena Gonzales
Kristina Grosso
Anna Hinck
Gaby Martinez
Gaby Miranda
Maxine Nocker
Nicole Parker
Cassidy Quinn
Destiny Rincon
Mia Ruvalcaba
Evelyn Teran
Victoria Tiburcio
Gisselle Valencia
Jaelynne Vega Camacho
Florence Wang
Indiya Zubiate

Table of Contents

This book was a collaborative effort
between the Gevirtz Graduate School of Education
and Girls Inc. of Greater Santa Barbara.

Note from the Editors

The word *scientist* was originated in 1833 by William Whewell, a professor who marveled over new work in physics by Mary Somerville and declared that the prevalent title "man of science" no longer fit the profile of those who were engaging in scientific work. Hence, today we refer to those in pursuit of truth about the nature and potential of our world and all living matter within it as *scientists*.

Women have long contributed to the development of new knowledge and innovations that benefit our world in many ways, some more visible than others. The 12 scientists and engineers of the University of California Santa Barbara who are featured within this volume represent the diversity of STEM* disciplinary research and development, building on the great discoveries and achievements by widely known figures such as Ada Lovelace and Marie Curie.

We are thrilled to provide you with the means of learning about the work of these current UCSB professors, researchers, and graduate students and their passions for advancing their respective fields. Additionally, you get to discover these scientists and their work through the eyes of 25 young women, ages 8 to 11, who were participants in the Curie-osity Project, an initiative that introduces young women in Grades 4 through 6 to the women scientists and engineers of the UCSB community.

*STEM is an abbreviation used primarily in education to unite the fields of Science, Technology, Engineering, and Mathematics.

From January to September of 2017, youth from Girls Inc. researched, interviewed, and wrote about these 12 women scientists and engineers. In the following pages, you will see the writing and artwork of our young, intrepid scholars. We cannot imagine a more effective way to celebrate the work that women are doing across science, technology, engineering, and mathematics today.

—Diana J. Arya, Assistant Professor in the Gevirtz Graduate School of Education and Director of the McEnroe Reading and Language Arts Clinic

—Jasmine K. McBeath, PhD student in the Gevirtz Graduate School of Education and Coordinator of the Curie-osity Project

STEMinists

The Lifework of 12 Women Scientists and Engineers

Biology

Jasmine Childress

Graduate Student Researcher

Parasitology

Jasmine Childress is a PhD student and researcher working in the Parasite Ecology Lab at UC Santa Barbara.

From a young age, Jasmine liked playing with different kinds of animals like lizards and other reptiles. She loved to play outside any chance she got. When talking about her favorite subjects in school, Jasmine said she loved math and recess the most.

When Jasmine got to college and started thinking about different careers, she had a hard time figuring out what to do. She did not see many women of color in science and this inspired her to change that. She decided to be a Parasitologist, which is someone who studies parasites and how they invade other animals.

Jasmine loves what she does. Some of the research her lab does is about parasites that infect marine animals' brains. One type of parasite she looks at are called trematodes. Jasmine explained, "Cercariae are types of trematodes that penetrates the fish's brain to make it swim all wonky." The parasite also makes it easier for fish to be eaten by birds because its brain is infected so it doesn't know how to protect itself. To look at these parasites, she takes infected snails and smashes their shells open, then she looks at them under a microscope and sees if the cercariae are infecting it.

Jasmine is a graduate student, so that means she wants to complete her very own research. This makes her really busy so she doesn't get much free time because she usually has to be studying or doing work. When she does get free time, she likes to play volleyball and ultimate frisbee. She also loves to play with puppies.

Ryoko Oono

Assistant Professor

Evolutionary Ecology

Dr. Ryoko Oono, a professor at UC Santa Barbara, worked very hard to be where she is now. She got her PhD from the University of Minnesota in Plant Biology and now works at UCSB where she experiments with plants. Ryoko studies "how plants interact with a diverse community of microbes in different environments." This means that she researches how plants and microbes work together in different ways depending on where they are. The coolest part of Ryoko's job is working with people and sharing new discoveries with them. If she thought she found a new microbial species, she would check if it had been previously described, and if not she would name the new species.

Ryoko likes to mentor students. She helped one of her students win a science fair project. She likes to help other people succeed. We did an experiment at her lab to grow microbes on a leaf. Plants have thousands of microbes. You can culture and grow many of them.

She became interested in plants because she was inspired by her parents' garden. She thought about being a photographer or an architect, but she also liked math and science and the pursuit of knowledge, so she decided to become a scientist. Aside from studying plants, Ryoko

The Young Scientist
Ryoko during a family vacation at Arches National Park in 1991.

likes being outdoors. She enjoys hiking and running and rock climbing. She also likes cooking. Relaxing is also very important to her.

Ryoko is a successful scientist who enjoys working with others and helping them to achieve their goals.

Alyson Santoro

Assistant Professor

Marine Microbiology

As a professor at UC Santa Barbara, Dr. Alyson Santoro has accomplished something that very few people have the opportunity to do: she named her own microbe! She named it *Candidatus* Nitrosopelagicus brevis. You may be wondering what a microbe is, well it is a type of organism that lives in the ocean and is so small you have to look through a microscope to see it. A cool fact about microbes is that if you stretch out all the microbes in the ocean they would circle the Milky Way. How cool is that?!

In order to make this huge accomplishment happen, Alyson went through many ups and downs. She was a waitress and worked at a bookstore before she became a Marine Biologist. Once she became a Marine Biologist, a lot of people doubted her and her ability to do science, so in order to prove them wrong, she had to work extremely hard to show how good she was.

Through her education at Dartmouth and Stanford, Alyson became interested in science and art. She took many courses related to science and eventually landed in Marine Biology. Now a professor at UCSB, Alyson is able to travel all over the world studying the ocean and microbes. One particular thing that is awesome about her traveling the world is the way she collects samples from the ocean.

The Young Scientist
Alyson swimming with her brother in 1987.

Alyson uses a special machine to collect samples called a rosette. When you put it in the water it opens up at different depths to collect water, and then back at the lab you look at the water samples under a microscope. After she looks through the microscope, Alyson decodes the microbes by looking up their DNA in a computer system. A cool way Alyson displayed this process was by having us create bracelets that used different colored beads to represent DNA.

As a child, Alyson grew up in New York and chose to go to school in California because she likes being outdoors. When she's not in the lab, Alyson celebrates her love for nature by going on adventures and hiking. She also has two German shepherds that she likes to take for walks. She also likes cooking, but is sure her dogs don't get any table scraps ... or do they?

Alyson is truly one of a kind as she represents that girls and women can do anything, especially science. Her hard work and dedication is inspirational and shows that no matter what, you can become a Marine Biologist and name your own microbe.

Geographic Sciences

Susan Cassels

Assistant Professor

Health Geography

Have you ever wondered why and how certain people get diseases? Well, Dr. Susan Cassels once wondered the same thing, and it led to a newfound passion and lasting career.

Susan was born in Seattle, Washington, but she left rainy Washington for sunny California to attend UC Santa

Barbara for her undergraduate work. Growing up, Susan was constantly changing her mind about what she wanted to do later in life, so she tried a variety of careers before becoming involved with the world of Human Geography, including being a lifeguard and a barista! When she was a kid, Susan's favorite subject in school was math, which perhaps inspired Susan to earn her BS in Mathematical Sciences with a minor in Music from UCSB. She earned her PhD in Demography from Princeton University, and she also has an MPH in Epidemiology from the University of Washington.

Susan is now a professor in the Geography Department at UCSB, where she studies the health of migrants and people who move to help explain and improve the ways that people can access health care and prevent ill health.

Susan noted that she struggled to plan for her future and didn't always have a clear vision, so she now feels that one

The Young Scientist
Susan showing a smile in her fourth-grade school picture.

of her proudest accomplishments is being able to help students earn their degrees and act as a mentor for them.

There's more to Susan than just her job though. Her favorite animal is a dolphin, and she has a pet dog named Rufus. Her favorite color is brownish-greenish ("like dirt!"), and in her spare time she loves to play soccer and go to the park with her son and daughter.

Vena Chu

Assistant Professor

Arctic Geography

Dr. Vena Chu is a Geographer who studies glaciers in Greenland. Before that though, she was an accountant. She was interested in business before she was inspired by a geography class about glaciers. She now studies the Arctic climate. She studies how it impacts hydrology—the study of Earth's water—and is particularly interested in Greenland's ice sheets.

Vena Chu

Vena likes music and attends a lot of concerts. She likes to watch TV shows and movies in her free time. The coolest part about her job is that she gets to help the planet by studying glaciers.

She uses computers to try to prevent the sea level from rising. Vena is inspiring because she was brave enough to change careers. Now she is a female scientist making new discoveries!

The Young Scientist

Vena standing tall
and ready at 9 years old.

Jennifer King

Professor

Biogeochemistry

Dr. Jennifer King grew up in Texas though her family originated from China. She is a female scientist who studies the environment. Jennifer went to Rice University and is currently teaching at UC Santa Barbara. She studies how plants decompose in different conditions, and she even gets to play with dirt and soil!

Jennifer King

As a young girl, Jennifer wanted to be a medical doctor. She used to work for the US Department of Agriculture. She got a PhD in Earth System Science and started working as a professor in Minnesota. Now she is a professor at UCSB in the Department of Geography and is a Biogeochemist. She does lots of work related to the carbon cycle. Her favorite part of her career is getting to work with her students.

Some recent projects have included measurements of greenhouse gases from agricultural systems, the impacts of solar radiation on decomposition of plants, and soil carbon accumulation in wetlands, such as the Carpinteria Salt Marsh. She collects samples so she can study the ecosystem.

The Young Scientist

Jennifer posing for her fourth-grade school picture.

In conclusion, Jennifer is a scientist and a professor who studies the decomposition of plants. She is passionate about her job, both in her research projects and working with her students.

Mathematics
Engineering
Computer Science

1 2 3 4

Katy Craig

Assistant Professor

Mathematics

Dr. Katy Craig was born in Dallas, Texas. She is a Mathematician who studies the common mathematical features of small groups and interactions, and develops new ways to predict their behavior using computers. Her research includes calculus and numerical analysis.

Katy Craig

When she was a little girl, Katy wanted to be an actress and was interested in theater. She had no idea she would grow up to be a mathematician. She got interested in math because, as a young girl, she did not like to memorize things but was good at puzzles.

When people doubt her, she stays headstrong and convinces them that she can do things. Her proudest accomplishment is becoming a professor at UC Santa Barbara because she went to school for many years. Before coming to UCSB, she attended Stanford, Rutgers, and UCLA. She also worked at Apple for two years, with a job in finance. Katy's favorite part of her job is getting to work with fun puzzles, and she believes that almost any game can be studied using math. During her presentation, we played a game based off of the TV game show *Let's Make a Deal*, called the Monty Hall Problem.

The Young Scientist
Katy smiling for the camera during the summer of 1997.

Katy has a daughter who she likes to play with, and in her spare time she likes to cook and bike.

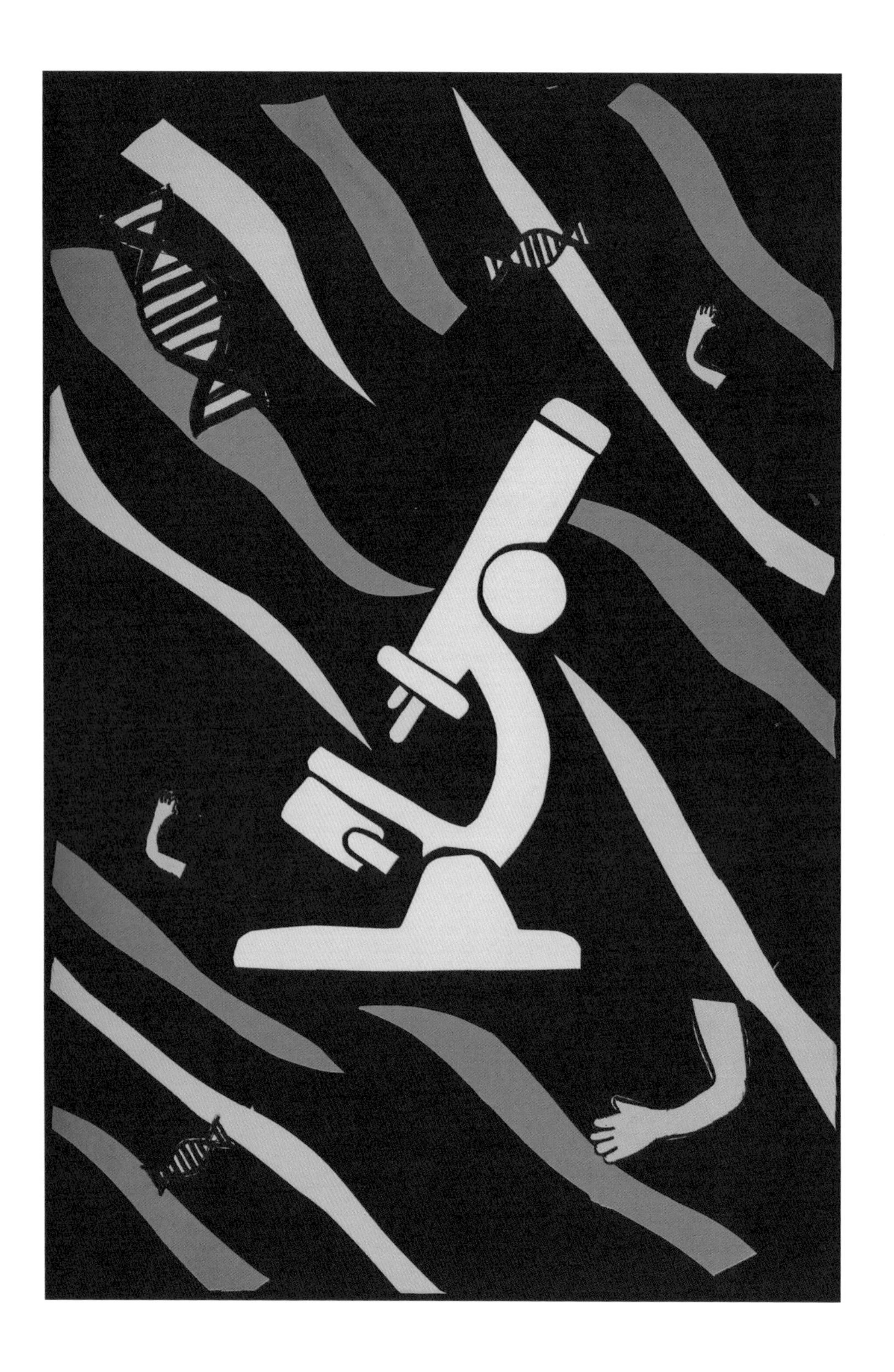

Adele Doyle

Lecturer and Researcher

Biomedical Engineering

Did you know that Dr. Adele Doyle likes to solve puzzles about malfunctioning organs and tissues?! Adele helps others by biomedically engineering body parts using stem cell research. She said, "I am glad to have found a way to contribute to society through my chosen career path and that my actions can help promote a more equitable and healthy society." Adele grew up in Oklahoma where she wanted to be a doctor, but discovered that biomedical engineering was a better fit when she went to Washington University in St. Louis for college. Her past jobs include working at a dairy store, delivering newspapers, tutoring, working in a research lab, and working in a multibillion-dollar biotech company. Now her job is being a professor.

Adele is a mommy and currently pregnant with a baby boy, and a professor at the same time. It is very inspiring that she is pregnant and still works at the university and works to help people. Adele is proud that her research lab at UC Santa Barbara—working with two other engineering labs, led by Kimberly Foster and Megan Valentine—recently got a big grant from the National Science Foundation to study how forces affect cells in the brain. For Adele, the favorite part of her job is using creativity to solve biomedical engineering challenges. She has often been in the minority because of her gender, but her mentors helped her believe she could achieve her dreams!

Adele's favorite color is indigo, and she loves Australian wallabies. She likes to cook, read, spend time with her family, and hike!

$E=MC^2$
$a^2+b^2=c^2$

Linda Petzold

Professor

Computer Science

How many women do you see working with computers?

Dr. Linda Petzold is one of the few women in her field. Sometimes people doubted her, but she never paid attention to the comments. She just kept working hard and she accomplished every goal she dreamed of.

Linda Petzold

Linda is now a researcher and professor at UC Santa Barbara. She was interested in math and engineering at a young age. Her dad always had slide rules—which are mechanical analog computers that are used as calculators—lying around the house, and she was curious about what you could do with those. Her love for math and solving problems made her interested in her field even though there were mostly men in computer engineering. A lot of people doubted her because they didn't think a woman should do those kinds of things, but she did it anyway.

Linda solves complex problems in her work. Some of these problems include studying circadian rhythms and how your blood coagulates after you get in an accident or get hurt. She mostly designs algorithms that solve these problems mathematically on a computer.

The tools that Linda creates help people do future research. Her team builds mathematical tools and computing tools that can help researchers in a lot of different fields. Not only do they help other engineers, but a lot of her work can help people in other scientific careers and in the medical field. These tools make the research easier because the computer figures out what's wrong much faster than humans can.

In her free time when she isn't teaching and doing research, Linda likes to hang out with her family and her dogs. She loves the work she does so she is almost always working, but she also likes to spend her free time playing on her iPad and figuring out different kinds of technology.

Neuroscience
Psychology

Liz Chrastil

Assistant Professor

Spatial Neuroscience

Brains, mazes, and research studies are all things Dr. Liz Chrastil knows and loves. You would not believe that when Liz was young, she wanted to be Michael Jackson or a gymnast when she grew up. Instead she ended up a Geographer who studies research on the brain. Her life is amazing. You see, she's a Neuroscientist but you're going to be wowed when you hear about her. Yah, wow!

Liz uses virtual reality mazes to study how the brain uses navigation. She likes making mazes and hiding objects in them that people can use. She uses wheelchairs to test people's brains instead of using muscle memory. Her work is inspiring in that she discovers new data. Liz has been working as a geography professor for one year. Her favorite part of the brain is the retrosplenial cortex, which deals with memory, though not a lot is known about this part of the brain. This is why she enjoys studying it!

Liz always used to doubt herself constantly, but by building her self-confidence she overcame it. "You can't do it" is a thought she had. But she defeated all her doubts, and poof—gone! She moved from Boston to California, she did it! Liz's proudest accomplishment was moving to California from Indiana and Boston.

The Young Scientist
Liz presenting her fifth-grade science project.

Some facts about Liz are that she loves to ride bikes, play guitar, dance, and also loves cats. Her favorite color is Neptune blue, and her favorite animals are lions and otters.

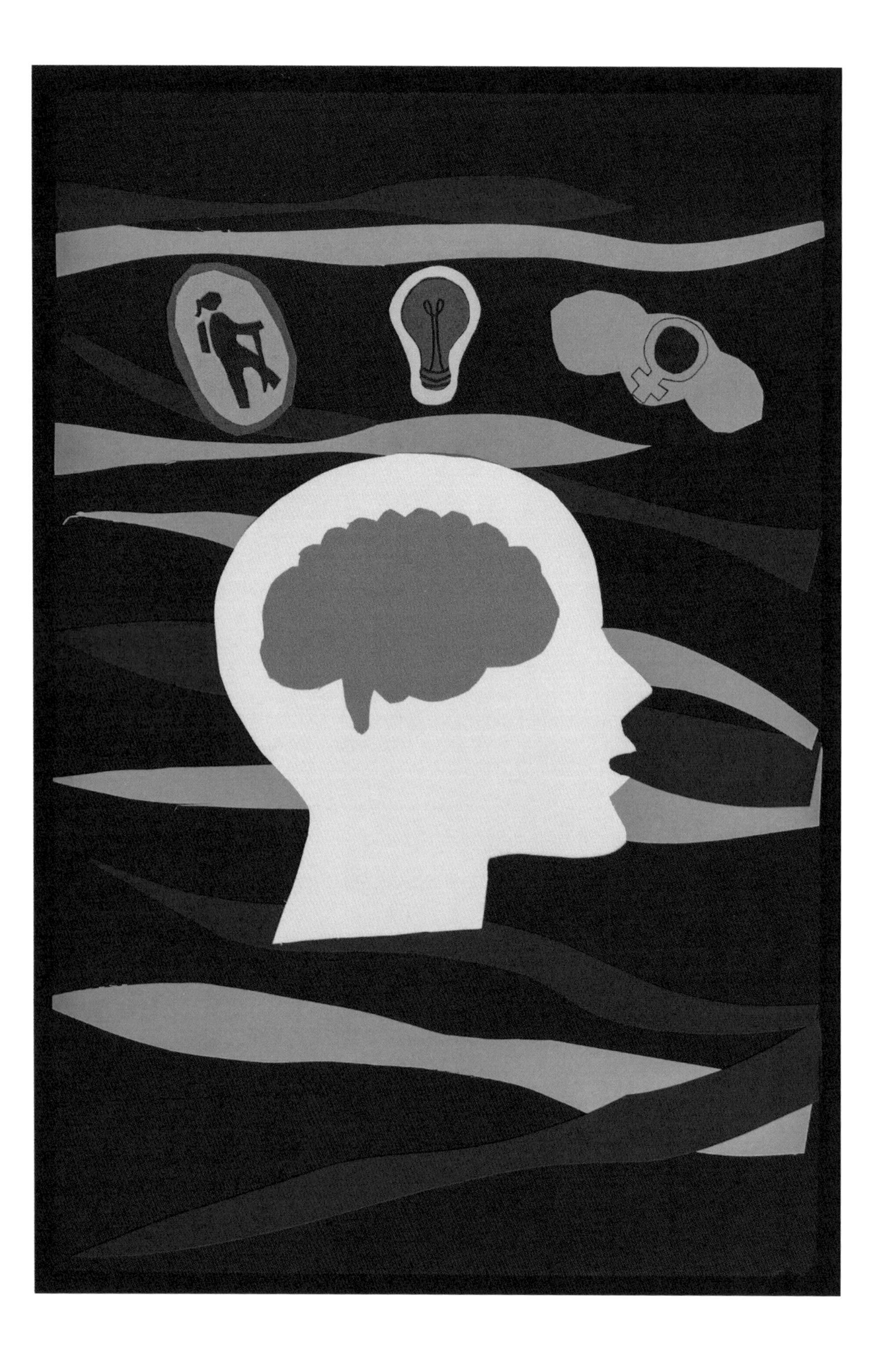

Emily Jacobs

Assistant Professor

Neuroscience

When she was a kid, Dr. Emily Jacobs wanted to be a "scientist who wore glitter." These days she doesn't always wear glitter, but her interest in and love for science is as strong as ever.

Emily grew up in Illinois and moved to Santa Barbara in 2016. Emily attended Smith College for undergrad where she earned her BA in Neuroscience. She then went on to UC Berkeley to earn her PhD in Neuroscience.

Emily is now a researcher and assistant professor at UCSB. She studies how men's and women's brains age differently, and the sense of discovery is her favorite part of her job. The most difficult part of her job is balancing lab work with all the other things professors do, like teaching, mentoring, and fundraising. She loves using the scientific method to bring new knowledge into the world that could improve the lives of women and men.

Emily notes that sometimes experiments confirm your hypotheses and other times they don't, but either way both outcomes provide valuable information. One of Emily's favorite parts of her job is having the opportunity to communicate discoveries to wide audiences. Emily's lab uses tools to measure brain structure and function, which contribute to her study of how hormones influence the brain.

The Young Scientist
Emily holding her favorite glittery Astronaut Barbie at 4 years old.

In her spare time, Emily loves to hike and explore in Santa Barbara with her daughter, and her favorite colors are green and gray. Even though she is not a scientist that wears glitter, she is proud of her accomplishments and what she has done in her lifetime. Emily is still discovering new things about differences in the brains of women and men!

Zoe Liberman

Assistant Professor

Developmental Psychology

"I study how babies make sense of the social world by looking at their expectations about how people will act and interact," explains Dr. Zoe Liberman. Zoe designs and performs experiments with babies to gather data on how babies think about social relationships and how their own background changes these experiences. She is super interested in how babies start to understand our complicated social world, like what types of features they use to think about social relationships. She studies how babies use information about people's social relationships to make predictions about how those people will act. For example, the language they hear at home can change their expectations.

Zoe is currently an assistant professor in the Department of Psychological and Brain Sciences at UC Santa Barbara, where researchers look at the structure of the human mind and how we think. She studies how babies think and how they make sense of our world. She received her BS, which is her Bachelor of Science, from Yale University, in Psychology. After that, she went to University of Chicago and got her PhD in Developmental Psychology, which is how she studies human development. She has liked science since she was little and did a research project on

The Young Scientist
Zoe spending her younger days at Oak Knoll Park in St. Louis.

a fly's eye. Her report on the fly's eye got published when she was in college. She even did a rocket competition!

Zoe loves babies, but she loves dogs as well. She is too busy to own her own dog, but goes to the beach to see dogs.

Girls, Inc. participants.

Curie-osity Authors

Craft 'n' Curious

Dino-mite Girls

Friends Group

Golden Science Masters

Puppies & Snow Leopards

Solar Lovelaces

Participant Voices

"Three words: interview, scientists, laughter, fun. I know that's more than three words."

"It was hard work, but it was really fun and we got to learn a lot about science in the process. It was very inspiring to do science and it was also a very interesting and very cool project."

"We worked hard and it took lots of time and we asked scientists questions."

"My favorite thing was how we got to interview the scientists and do the activities."

"Buy this book, it's interesting, very interesting!"

"I thought it was really interesting and fun and I wanted to do it again."

"My favorite part was ... let me think ... I remember I made the intestine crown for Anna."

"Basically, you would interview scientists and we had little activities to help us learn about what they were doing and we would take notes and write about them."

Acknowledgments

girls inc.

of Greater Santa Barbara

Acknowledgments

If it were not for the following people, this project may not have happened. Our sincerest gratitude to the following individuals.

Curie-osity Project Principal Investigators:
Diana J. Arya
Danielle Harlow

Curie-osity Project Coordinator:
Jasmine K. McBeath

UCSB Coordination and Project Consultation Support:
Valerie Meier
George Yatchinson
Lois Harmon

Girls Inc. Leadership and Coordination Support:
Kristen Webster
Phyllis Amerikaner
Kristen Weaver

UCSB Undergraduate Instructional Support Team:

Abby Brenneman
Anna To
Diana Mejia-Whistler
Jasmine Lovette
Kate Cella
Maya Longtin
Yessica Ramirez
Amy Chen
Darien Perez
Gina Roitman
Joi Duncan
Lizeth Godoy
Tiffany Edwards-Jordan
Yinxuan Gu

Girls Inc. Support Staff:

Heidi Diaz
Nicole Zamanzadeh
Samantha Eddy
Lilia Sosa
Rosa Ruiz
Skip Gaffke

Art Director: Douglas Keith

Writing Director: Sarah Hirsch

Guest Instructor: Nell Campbell, Photographer

Assessment Support:

Jenny Sperling
Oaram Kim
Jim Gribble
Zeinab Halawi

Community Supporters:
Nestor Covarrubias (UCSB Transportation Services)
Rick Benjamin (Community Engagement)

Finally, we are ever grateful to Tina and Paul McEnroe, cofounders of the McEnroe Reading and Language Arts Clinic within the Gevirtz Graduate School of Education, which served as the primary site for all Curie-osity activities. Thank you, Tina and Paul, for your commitment to our community's children and for supporting the publication of this book.

Tina Hansen McEnroe and Paul V. McEnroe
Reading & Language Arts Clinic

Index

Index A–C

Index D–F

Index G–L

Index M–O

Index P–S

Index T–Z

Made in the USA
Columbia, SC
16 April 2018